DOMENICO SCARLATTI

ELEVEN SONATAS

Edited by Howard Ferguson

(The Kp-numbers refer to the possible chronological order proposed by Ralph Kirkpatrick in his important book, *Domenico Scarlatti*; Princeton 1953.)

ABRSM

Published by ABRSM (Publishing) Ltd, a wholly owned subsidiary of ABRSM
Printed in England by Halstan & Co. Ltd, Amersham, Bucks., on materials from sustainable sources
Reprinted in 2017

INTRODUCTION

Domenico Scarlatti (1685-1757)

Domenico Scarlatti, son of the Neapolitan opera composer Alessandro, was born in the same year as Bach and Handel. His early manhood was spent in various posts in Naples, Venice and Rome; then, at about the age of 34, he became *maestro* of the Portugese royal chapel, and harpsichord teacher to the King's eldest daughter, the Infanta Maria Barbara. On her marriage in 1728 to Fernando, heir to the Spanish throne, he moved with the rest of the Princess's entourage to Madrid, where he remained for the rest of his life.

Though he had composed vocal, instrumental, and operatic works while still in Italy, Scarlatti is known today almost entirely by the 555 harpsichord Sonatas (mostly in single-movement binary form) that he is thought to have written mainly after his arrival in the Iberian Peninsula. Strangely enough, none of the Sonatas has survived in autograph. Some seventy were published in London, Amsterdam and Paris between 1728 and Scarlatti's death; but the majority are known only through contemporary manuscript copies. The most important of these are contained in two collections: (1) the 15 sumptuously-bound volumes that belonged to the Queen of Spain (now in Venice, Biblioteca Nationale Marciana, 9770-84); and (2) a similar though not identical set of 15 volumes, whose original owner is unknown (Parma, Conservatorio di Musica Arrigo Boito, AG 31406-20).[1]

The present texts are taken from the Parma MSS, with the exception of No.8 from the 'Worgan MS' (British Library, Add. MS.31553). Since there are no dynamics in the originals and almost no marks of articulation (slurs and staccatos), these have been added by the editor. The full words *forte* and *piano* here indicate the broad contrasts obtainable on a two-manual harpsichord, and hence the general dynamic level of a passage, section or complete piece. The remaining signs (*f, mf, mp, p, cresc., dim.,* ◁— —▷) show the type of gradations that a pianist (as distinct from a harpsichordist) might make within these limits. The articulation, which is of the utmost importance in Scarlatti, is such as might have been used by one of his contemporaries. A suggested interpretation of each ornament is shown above or below the stave at its first appearance in every piece. Note, however, that Scarlatti's ornamentation depends more on its context than on the particular sign used: so a single ornament is sometimes interpreted in two different ways, and two different ornaments in a single way. This is intentional. An editorial metronome mark has been added at the end of each piece; it should be understood, however, that it is neither authoritative nor binding. Numbered footnotes are concerned with textual matters and lettered footnotes with interpretation.

HOWARD FERGUSON
Cambridge 1987

[1]Complete facsimile edition, based mainly on the Parma MSS: Domenico Scarlatti, *Complete Keyboard Works*, vols.1-18, ed. Ralph Kirkpatrick; Johnson Reprint Corporation, New York & London 1972. Complete modern edition, based mainly on the Venice MSS: Domenico Scarlatti, *Sonates*, vols.1-11, ed. Kenneth Gilbert; Heugel, Paris 1971-84.

ELEVEN SONATAS
Sonata in B flat
Kp.172

SCARLATTI

(a) The pause in b.20 implies a slight *rit.* in the bar before.

1) B.20, l.h. chord 1: the lower F is missing in the source, but shown in the Venice MS.

(b) The interpretation of Scarlatti's *Tremolo* (or *tre*) remains uncertain; but probably it implied a shake of some kind. In b.46, etc. it should presumably stop on the 4th quaver, since the Cs are untied.

2) B.57, l.h. note 2: the source has a natural to the A, not a flat – an obvious slip.

(c) L.h. bb.74 & 140:

[♩. = c.92]

Sonata in D minor

Kp.434

(a) B.17, l.h. note 6: the source has A; but see the more probable b.12

(b) In bb.50–51, etc., the editorial division between the two hands is suggested in order to preserve the individuality of the parts.

Sonata in A minor

Kp.149

1) The r.h. staccatos in bb.6, 7 & 12 are in the source.

[♩ = c.88]

Sonata in A

Kp.279

1) The slurs in r.h. bb.38, 40 & 42 (except the second in b.38) are in the source.

Sonata in D

Kp.277

(a) Note that many of the phrases in this sonata start with an upbeat crotchet, as shown by the upper slur in bb.4–6.

[♩ = c.92]

1) Bb.21–22, r.h.: the 3-note slurs are in the source.

2) B.22, r.h. upper line final note: the source has B; the more practicable G sharp is from the Münster MS.

3) B.39, r.h. note 4: the source has C (sharp), which was probably a slip.

Sonata in G†

Kp.424

† Many of the sonatas that are neighbours in the source and share the same tonic were almost certainly meant to be grouped together in performance. The present Nos. 6 & 7 form one such pair.

(a) A slight *rit.* is needed in b. 18.

(a) or: ; also in b.44, but with 3rd finger on r.h. note 1.

[♩ = c.88]

Sonata in G†

Kp.425

† See the footnote to the previous Sonata.

1) B.16, r.h. note 3: the source has G, not A: obviously a slip.

(a) A *rit.* is needed during bb.103–105.

2) B.138, r.h.: the source repeats the previous bar; but see bb.128, 130 & 136.

[♩. = c.84]

Sonata in G†

Kp.144

† The only source of this Sonata (the 'Worgan MS') is full of mistakes: hence the present emendations.

1) B.1, r.h. beat 4: the source has [notation], which seems improbable (see footnote 3).

2) B.6, l.h. chord 1: in the source the upper note is E, not G.

3) Bb.19–20: in the source these are shown as a single bar, with l.h. quavers and r.h. note-values ♩ ♫ ♪♫ ♫♫ (see footnote 1).

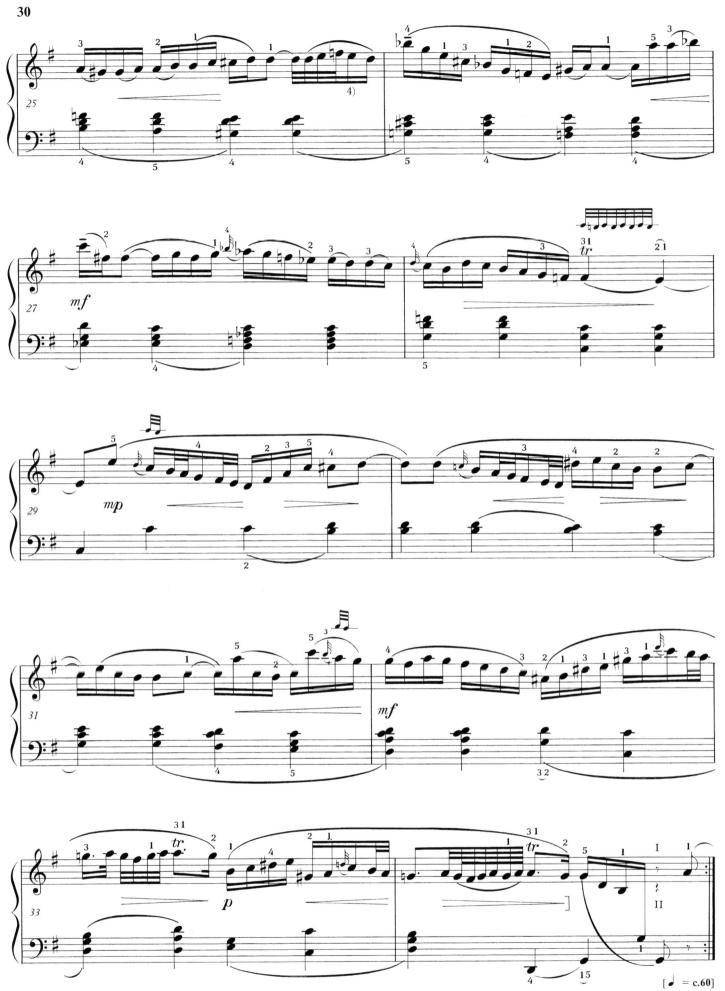

4) B.25, r.h.: the last two notes are quavers in the source.

[♩ = c.60]

Sonata in D

Kp.178

Sonata in B minor

Kp.197

1) B.35: the second half of the bar, which is missing in the source, has been added by analogy with b.18.

Sonata in G†

Kp.284

† One of the comparatively few Scarlatti sonatas *not* in binary form. It is a sort of rondo, alternating major and minor. The main theme (bb.1–8, 33–40, etc.) is continued differently at each of its appearances. The tempo should be set by bb.163–4, otherwise the beginning is likely to be too quick.

38

THEMATIC INDEX